GW00858093

A TREASURY OF BIBLE STORIES

An Hachette UK Company
www.hachette.co.uk

First published in Great Britain in 2017 by Bounty Books,
a division of Octopus Publishing Group Ltd
Carmelite House, 50 Victoria Embankment,
London EC4Y 0DZ
www.octopusbooks.co.uk

This material was first published in the *My Bible Stories* series in 2013, 2014 by
Tick Tock, a division of Octopus Publishing Group Ltd

ISBN 978-0-7537-3241-0

A CIP catalogue record for this book is available from the British Library

Printed and bound in China

10 9 8 7 6 5 4 3 2 1

For the Bounty edition
Publisher: Lucy Pessell
Designer: Lisa Layton
Editor: Sarah Vaughan
Production Controller: Meskerem Berhane

A TREASURY OF BIBLE STORIES

EIGHT OF YOUR VERY FAVOURITE TALES

This book belongs to:

.....Phoebe Therese Baxter.....

.....love from mummy..... 8/02/2020

CONTENTS

NOAH'S ARK

Written by Sasha Morton
Illustrated by Alfredo Belli

Long before the time of Jesus, there lived a man named Noah.
He and his family lived in a way that made God very happy.

But other people in the world
were fighting, stealing and arguing.
This made God very sad.

One day, God spoke to Noah. He wanted to put an end to the evil that was ruining the world and he needed Noah's help.

He asked Noah and his family to collect a pair of animals
from every species on Earth. Then he asked Noah
to build an enormous ark, on which they would all fit.
God was going to send a flood to wash away all the evil.

Noah and his family set
to work straight away.

They gathered two of
every animal and kept
them safe until their new
home was ready.

Next, they began to build the enormous ark. They chopped, sawed and hammered until after a great deal of hard work...

...it was finally ready!
As soon as the ark was complete, the sky grew dark,
the air grew still and the birds stopped twittering in the trees...

...and a heavy rain began.

Noah and his family
led the animals aboard
the ark and they waited.

The rain fell and fell and soon
the ark rose up and began to float!

Huge drops of rain fell from the sky until everything on the Earth was covered with water, even the mountain tops.

Everything would be washed away by the great flood.

Life on the ark was hard, especially with
so many animals to feed and keep clean.

Noah's family were tired and worried.
"Will the rain ever stop, Noah?" asked his wife.
"It is all part of God's plan," said Noah, as he looked out at the rising seas.

But as the days passed, they wondered if they would ever leave the ark again.

It rained for forty days and forty nights, and then as suddenly as it had started, the rain stopped!

The sun began to shine through the clouds and a swift wind blew.

As they drifted across the endless ocean,
Noah saw something above the water...

...it was land!

The ark drifted over to the top of the mountain. Then Noah quickly released a dove to see if it would find any more dry land.

They watched as the dove flew up
and over the horizon, then they waited.

But the dove soon flew back,
for there was nowhere for it to land.

After a week, Noah sent the dove out once more.

They watched the bird fly up and away, and before long, the dove came back carrying an olive branch!

It must have found a tree above the water!

The dove dropped the branch, then it flew from the ark and did not come back. Noah realised the land was dry enough to live on again.

It was time for their new lives to begin at last.

After many days at sea, the great flood was over. Noah stepped onto dry land and led his family and all the animals into a new world.

Noah and his family knelt down
and thanked God for saving them.
They promised to create a peaceful new world,
which would make God happy.

To reward him, God made Noah a promise.

He said, "I will never again send a flood to destroy the world. Instead, every time it rains, I will send a rainbow as a symbol to remind all living creatures on Earth that I will always keep them safe."

And to this day, God is true to his word. For whenever sun and rain appear in the sky together, a rainbow does indeed shine over the world.

JOSEPH
AND HIS COAT OF MANY COLOURS

Written by Sasha Morton
Illustrated by Cherie Zamazing

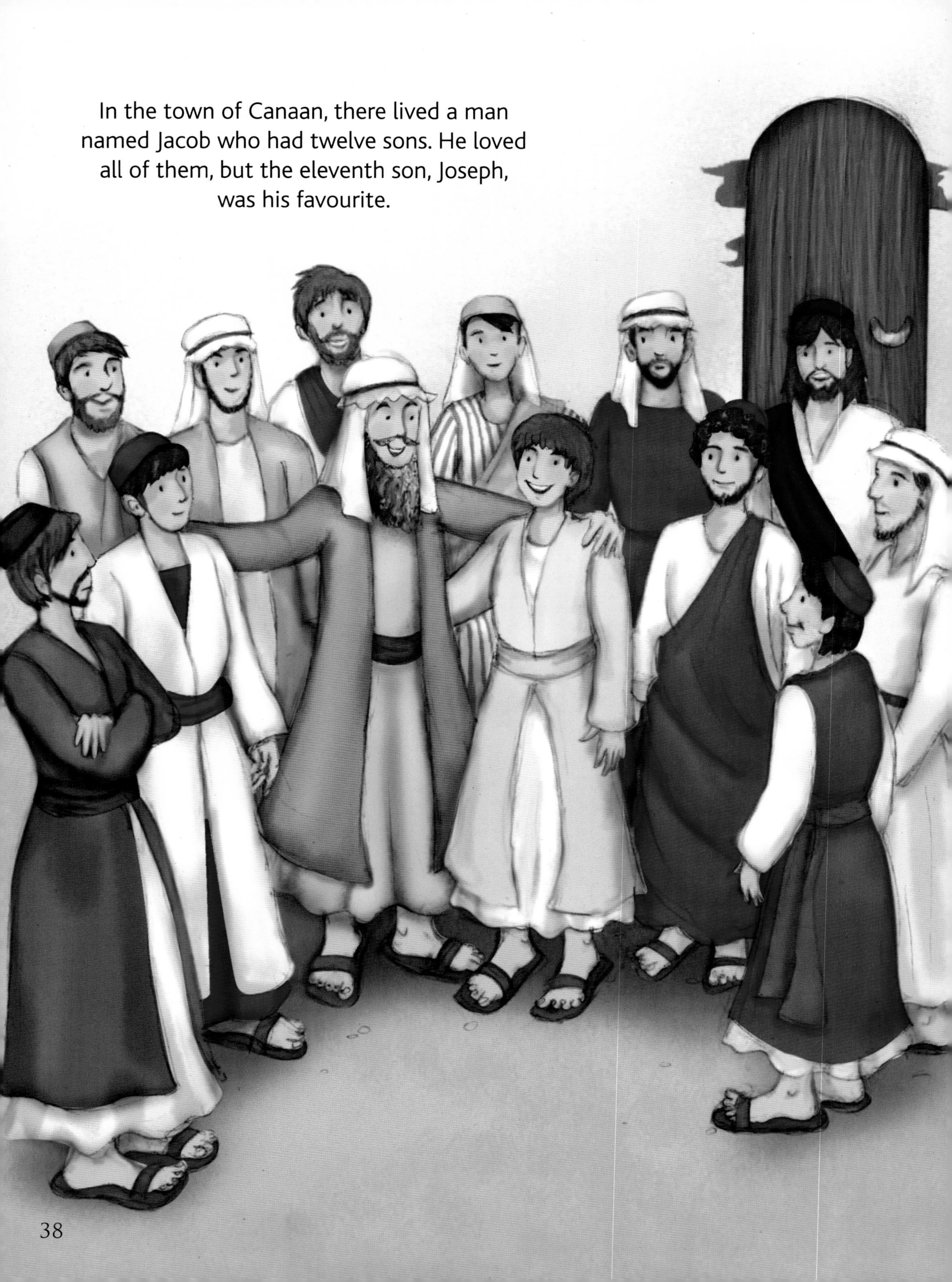

In the town of Canaan, there lived a man named Jacob who had twelve sons. He loved all of them, but the eleventh son, Joseph, was his favourite.

Joseph had dreams that he would share with his family. Sometimes, these dreams made his brothers angry, because in them, Joseph seemed to rule over everyone else.

Joseph's brothers were also very jealous because he had been given a beautiful coat by their father.

One day, when the brothers were tending their sheep, they saw Joseph walking towards them wearing his coloured coat.

In anger, the cruel brothers ripped Joseph's coat from him and threw him into an old, dry well!

But they were undecided what to do with their prisoner...

"We must not kill him," said one of the brothers.
Then he saw some men approaching with heavily laden camels. "But perhaps we could sell him to these traders?"

So Joseph was dragged from the well, sold and taken to Egypt.

To explain his disappearance, the brothers smeared Joseph's coat with goat's blood, and took it back to their father.

The brothers told their father, Jacob, that Joseph was killed by a wild animal. Jacob believed them. He was devastated to have lost his favourite child.

Little did Jacob know his son had been sold as a slave!

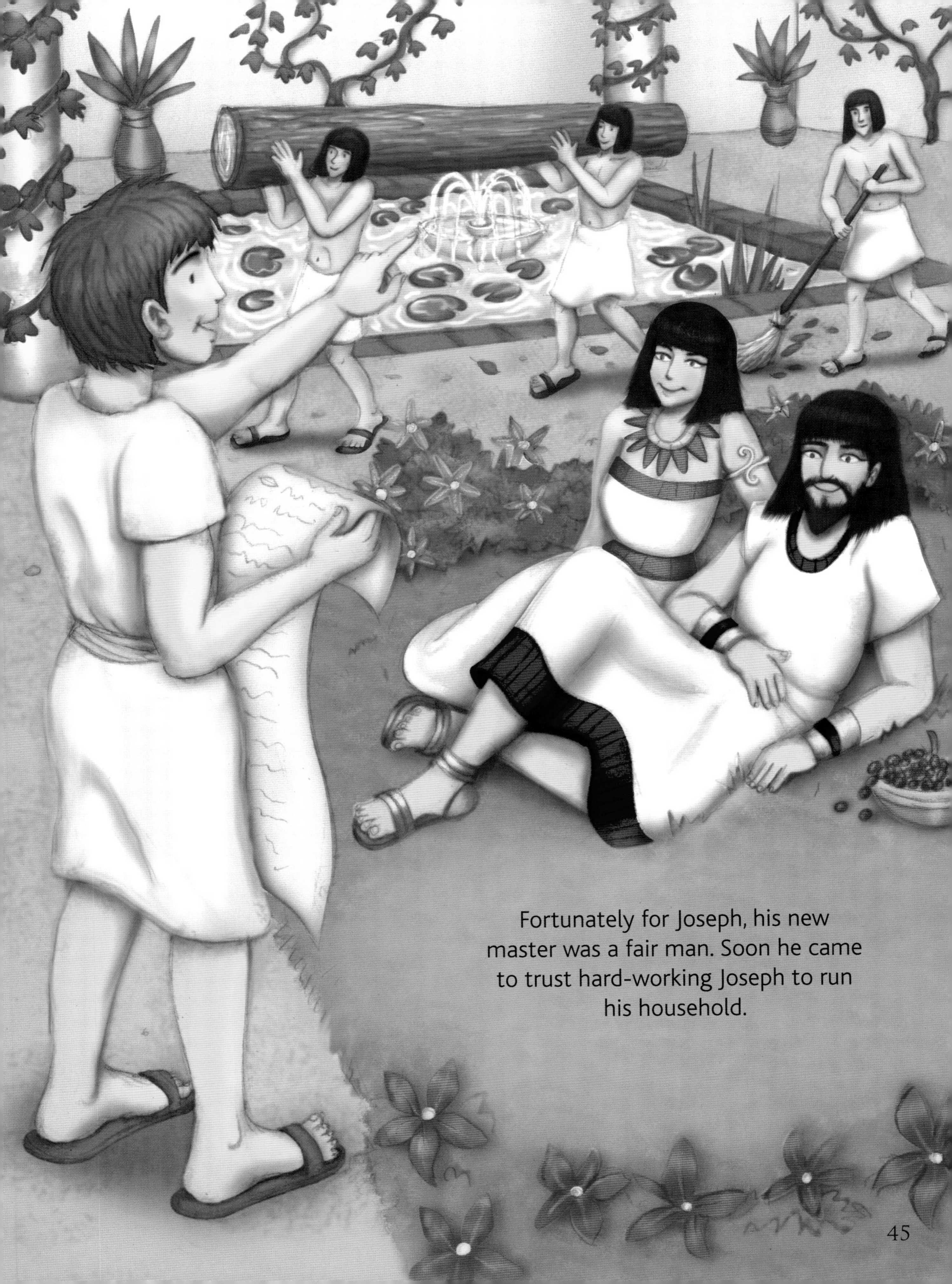

Fortunately for Joseph, his new master was a fair man. Soon he came to trust hard-working Joseph to run his household.

Time passed, and Joseph was tricked by a wicked woman and sent to prison. But God continued to help Joseph explain people's dreams. Word of this gift from God spread to the Pharaoh.

Troubled by dreams of his own, the Pharaoh sent for Joseph. "In my dreams, I see seven thin cows eat seven fat cows," explained the Pharaoh to Joseph.

“Then I see seven ripe ears of corn being swallowed by seven broken ears of corn. What can this mean?”

Joseph thought the dream had been sent by God, and told the Pharaoh, "Seven years of plenty are coming, but they will be followed by seven years of famine. God wants you to prepare Egypt for what lies ahead."

Joseph continued, "You should store food in the seven good years. This food will feed your people during the seven years of famine."

The Pharaoh was so grateful for Joseph's advice that he made him the governor of Egypt. It was Joseph's job to travel throughout the land, helping people to get ready for the famine.

Once more, Joseph served his master well. He was the second most important man in Egypt, and became rich during those seven years of hard work.

And after those seven good years, just as the dream had predicted, the famine began. Thanks to Joseph's planning and storing, no one in Egypt went hungry.

But in Canaan, after two years, there was nothing left to eat and no crops would grow in the parched soil.

Joseph's brothers had no choice but to travel to Egypt to buy grain to make bread for their starving family.

As the person in charge of selling grain to anyone who came to Egypt in need of food, Joseph watched his brothers bow before him. Not one of them recognised the brother they had sold into slavery.

Joseph said nothing, but sold them the grain they had come to him for. He knew that the famine would continue, and that they would return again.

When Jacob sent his sons to Egypt the next time, Joseph stood before them and said, "I am Joseph. Is my father still alive?"

All of the brothers were amazed to see Joseph was still alive. They wept and said sorry for what they had done to him. With a glad heart, Joseph forgave them.

"What happened to me was all part of God's plan to save many lives," he explained. "There are five more years of famine to come, but I have stored enough food for everyone. Do not blame yourselves for what you did."

The Pharaoh was so grateful to Joseph for keeping his people safe from hunger, he told him his family could come and live in Egypt too. Joseph proudly sent his brothers home to Canaan to bring back their father and their families.

It was only when Jacob saw Joseph with his own eyes that he realised his dream had come true: his son was alive.

"Now I can die in peace," wept Jacob as he hugged his long-lost son.

And they lived happy lives as a family once more.

THE STORY OF MOSES

Written by Sasha Morton
Illustrated by Cherie Zamazing

A long time ago in Egypt, a princess found an Israelite baby floating in a basket beside the riverbank near her palace.

His mother had hidden him away because the Pharaoh wanted all the boy Israelite babies to be killed.

The Pharaoh's kindly daughter adopted the baby and called him Moses, and so an Israelite boy grew up as a member of the Egyptian royal family.

But one day, Moses learned who he really was and became angry about how his people were treated.

Moses fled from the wicked Pharaoh. He wandered alone in the desert for many years, married a woman and had a child.

One day, he saw the strangest sight. A bush was on fire and a voice from within the flames was saying, "Moses, you must free the Israelites!"

"Who do I say sent me?"

gasped Moses in disbelief.

"I AM who I AM," boomed the voice of God. "And with my help, you will lead the Pharaoh's slaves out of Egypt, to a land where they can live in freedom."

"Ask the Pharaoh to release his slaves. He will not listen, but you should drop your staff to the floor. It will turn into a snake and then he may believe that I have sent you," said God.

As God had predicted, the Pharaoh refused to listen to Moses.
He wasn't even persuaded by the staff turning into a snake!
So God sent another message...

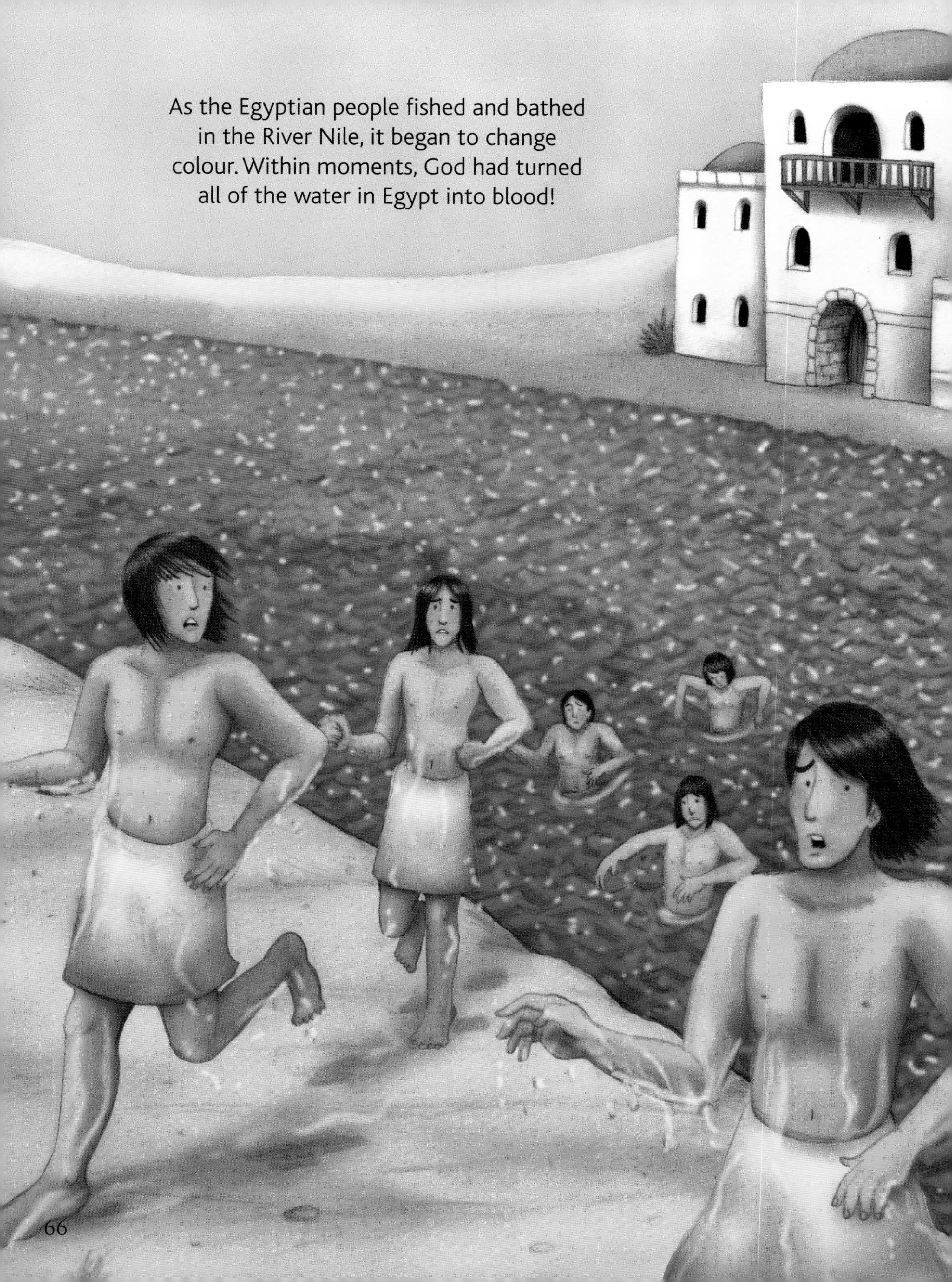

As the Egyptian people fished and bathed in the River Nile, it began to change colour. Within moments, God had turned all of the water in Egypt into blood!

There was no clean water to wash in or to drink.
But worse was soon to come.

For every day that the Pharaoh refused to free the Israelites, God sent a terrible plague into Egypt.

Frogs rained down,
mosquitos bit everyone
and flies made all the Egyptians itch.

Their cattle died,

boils made their skin sore

and hailstones, heavy
enough to shatter trees,
fell from the skies.

By now, every Egyptian wanted
the Pharaoh to set his slaves free,
but the Pharaoh refused.

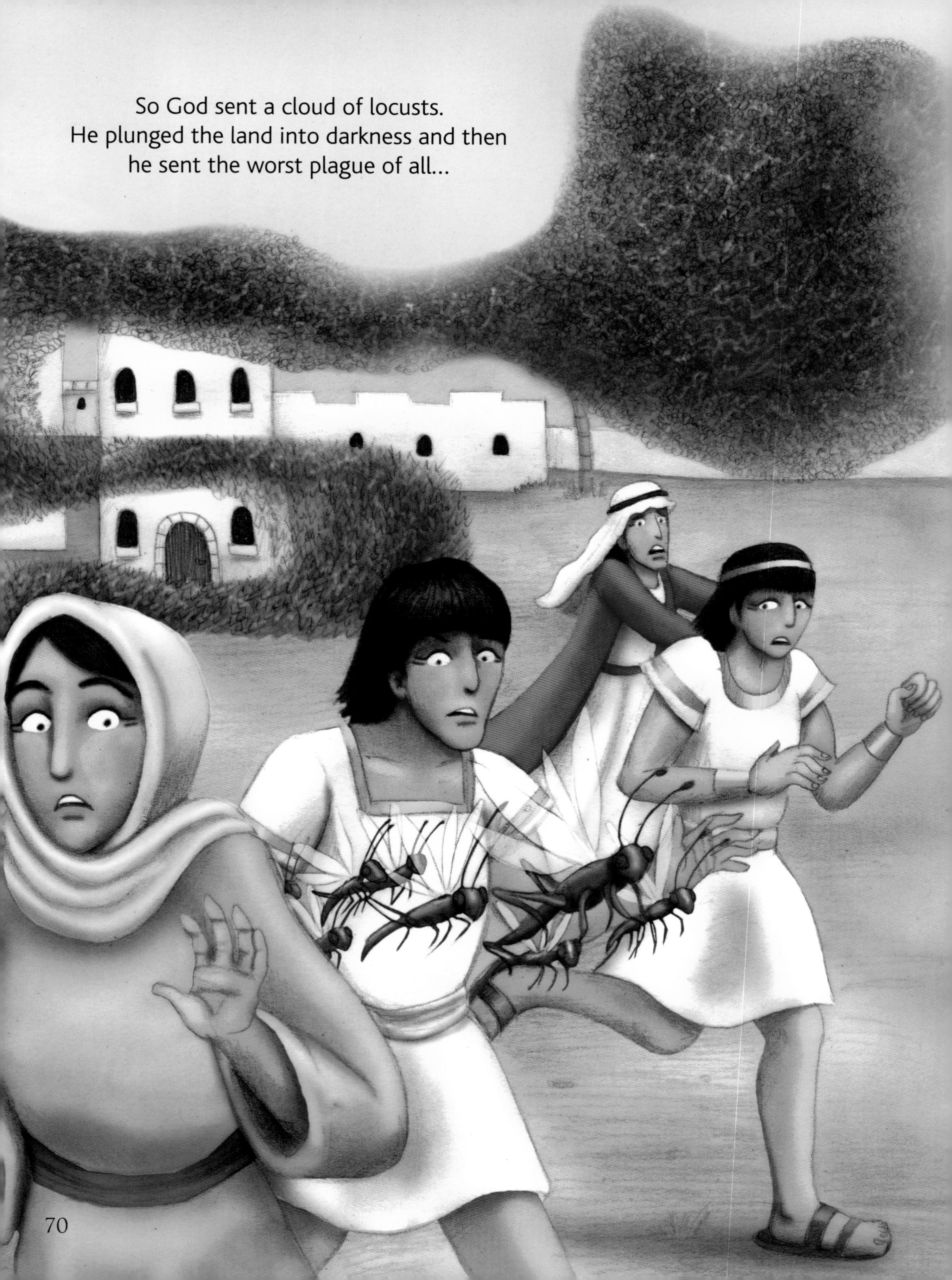

So God sent a cloud of locusts.
He plunged the land into darkness and then
he sent the worst plague of all...

Every firstborn Egyptian child died, including the Pharaoh's own son.

At last, the ruler gave in. Moses could lead the Israelites to God's Promised Land.

They were free at last!

God sent a pillar of cloud by day and
a pillar of fire by night to guide Moses
and his people through the desert.

But as they reached the edge of the Red Sea, the Israelites looked around in fear. Every soldier in the Egyptian army was racing across the desert to capture them!

The Pharaoh had changed his mind. Who would build and clean his palaces? He needed those slaves back!

Moses' people were in despair, some even thought they should go back to the Pharaoh. They were trapped, with the Red Sea before them and six hundred chariots behind them!

But God had told Moses what to do.

"Have no fear," said Moses, as he lifted his rod and stretched his hand out over the sea. To everyone's astonishment, the waves drew back to make two walls of water. Before them was a dry path that would lead the Israelites to freedom at last!

Quickly, the Israelites fled through the tunnel of water. The Egyptian army tried to follow them, but God's pillar of cloud swirled around the soldiers, confusing them.

Once Moses' people had safely crossed the Red Sea,
God lifted the cloud and the army charged after them.

As soon as every chariot was on the path, Moses raised his hand again.
The two huge walls of water tumbled back together and within moments,
the entire army was washed away!

How the Israelites cheered!
Together, they joined Moses in prayer
and thanked God for their freedom.

Moses led the Israelites through the wilderness for three long months. At last, God sent for Moses to come to the top of a mountain so he could speak with him.

While a fire burned brightly at the top of Mount Sinai, Moses' people waited for their leader to return to them.

Moses was up on the mountain for forty days and forty nights. When he returned, he brought a gift from God. Written on two stone tablets by the Lord himself were ten special laws that God wanted his people to live by.

And carrying these Commandments with them, the people who once were slaves set off to live in freedom, just as God himself had promised.

DAVID AND GOLIATH

Written by Sasha Morton
Illustrated by Alfredo Belli

Many years ago in Israel, there lived a boy named David who was the youngest of eight brothers. David spent his days quietly tending to his family's sheep and working as an armour-bearer for the king.

No one knew that David frightened off bears and lions that tried to attack his flock, using only his trusty slingshot. David may have been young, but he had very good aim.

Saul, the King of Israel, looked after his people well, but he was also very worried. Nearby, a huge army was waiting to fight his soldiers.

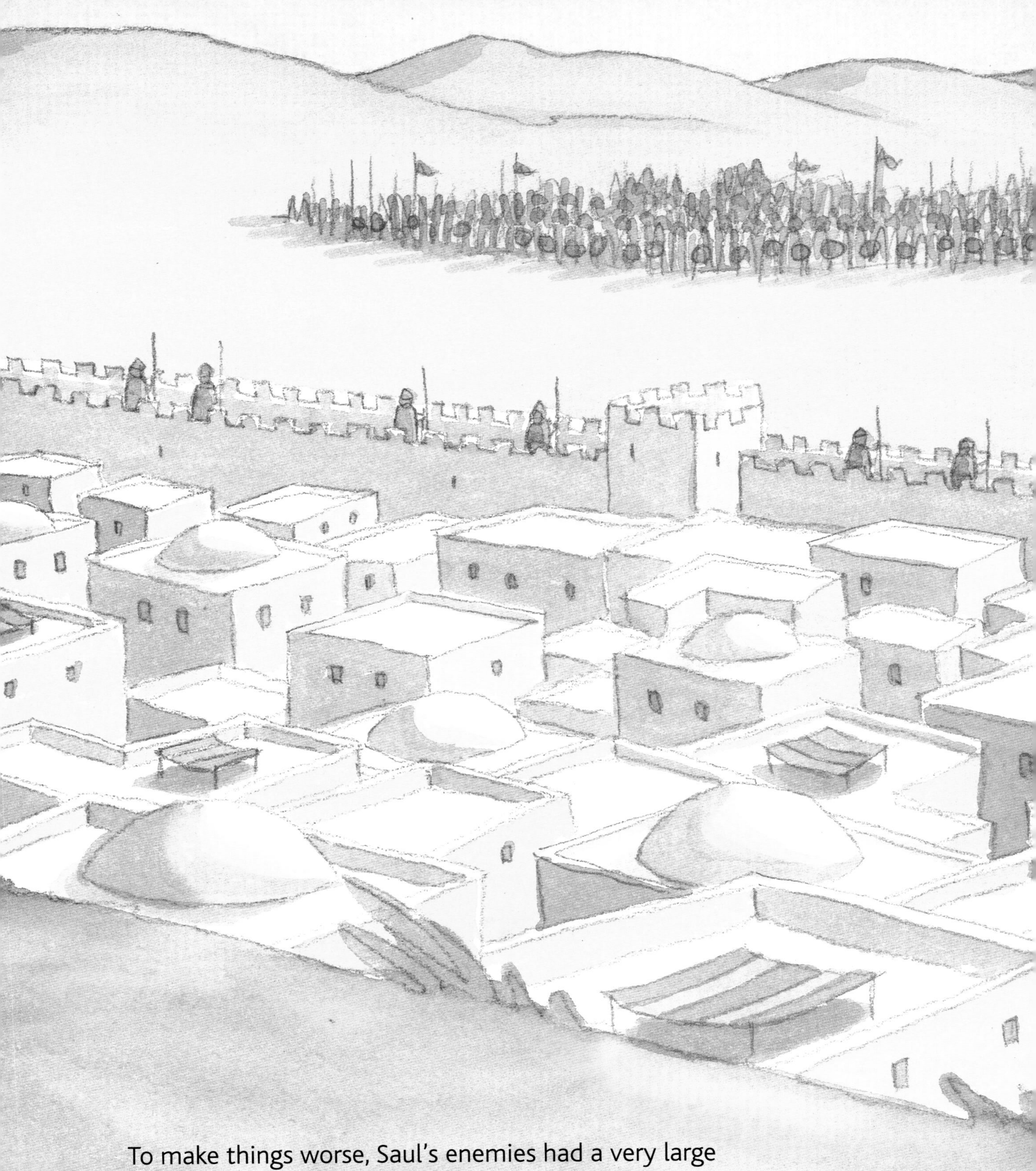

To make things worse, Saul's enemies had a very large and fearsome soldier on their side. His name was...

...GOLIATH!

Goliath towered over everyone around him and wore heavy metal armour. His spear was the size of a tree and wherever he walked, the land shook beneath his feet. He was terrifying!

"Send a man to fight me!" he roared to Saul's army. But no one would go near him. Days passed and nobody was strong enough to fight this enormous giant.

For forty days Goliath thundered onto the battlefield shouting, "Send a man to fight me! If he beats me, our people will be your slaves. If I defeat him, your people will become our servants."

Saul even offered a huge reward to anybody who would fight Goliath, but still nobody was brave enough to try.

One morning, Goliath stood between the two armies and shouted his usual threat.

Saul's soldiers were terrified, but on this day, it just so happened that David was visiting his brothers in the army camp. David grew angry. He was fed up of hearing this giant insult his people, who worked hard and put their faith in God to protect them.
It was time for someone to fight back!

David went to Saul and said,
"I, your servant, will fight this giant."

"David, you are only a boy, and Goliath has been a warrior his entire life!" gasped the king.

"That may be," replied David. "But if God can protect me while I keep my sheep safe, he will protect me in a battle against this enemy too."

Everyone was shocked that David would even try to fight Goliath, but they helped get him ready for the battle.

Saul dressed David in his own golden armour and gave David his magnificent sword. However, when David tried to walk, he made a surprising discovery...

...he could not move! David took off the shining armour and handed it back to Saul.

"What will you take to protect you?" asked the worried king.

David held up his trusty slingshot. "Just this," he replied firmly. David carefully chose five smooth stones from the nearby riverbed. He tucked them into his shepherd's pouch, and with only his sling in his hand, went to meet Goliath.

David took a deep breath and began to walk across the battlefield, where Goliath was waiting to fight. As he drew closer, Goliath began to laugh.

"You are the warrior that
Saul has sent to fight me?"
he bellowed in disbelief.

"You may raise a sword and a spear at me," David called up at him, "but I stand here in the name of the Lord."

With that, David slid a stone into his sling.

The smooth stone span through the air.

The soldiers on both sides gasped
and held their breath...

...and David's aim, as ever, was true.

The stone hit Goliath right in the forehead!
For a moment he stood completely still.

Then with a stagger, a stumble and an almighty crash,
Goliath fell down to the ground.

The enemy had been defeated!

Saul's soldiers chased their enemies out of Israel, and the whole land celebrated!

Even David's seven older brothers had to admit that they were proud of their quiet little brother.

David fought in many more battles and he always had faith that God would protect him. Many years later, David became the King of Israel, but he would always be remembered as the small boy who defeated a giant.

DANIEL
IN THE
LIONS' DEN

Written by Sasha Morton
Illustrated by Alfredo Belli

A long time ago, there lived a wise king named Darius.
He relied on a kind man called Daniel.
Daniel did all of the King's important jobs.

Unfortunately, three men who also worked
at the palace were jealous of Daniel.
They began to think about ways to turn
King Darius against him.

Daniel's work was always perfect, so they couldn't use that as a reason to get rid of him.

But the men knew that Daniel prayed to his God three times a day. So they decided to make it a crime to pray to anyone other than King Darius.

If Daniel was caught praying to his God, they would be able to punish him by throwing him into the lions' den!

The men went to King Darius and said, "We have written a new law. It says that if anyone is caught praying to someone other than you they shall be thrown to the lions. Will you sign these papers to make it so?"

King Darius readily signed the papers, not realising what it would mean.

That night, Daniel prayed to his God, as he always did.

He had no idea he was being spied on.

The men went straight to the King and told him what they had seen. With a heavy heart, King Darius realised that Daniel must be punished for praying to someone other than him.

He had passed the law himself. What else could he do?

Daniel was still deep in prayer when three guards crashed into his room, shouting, "By praying to your God you have broken the King's law. Your punishment is to be thrown to the lions."

With that, the guards tied Daniel's
hands and marched him straight
to the palace.

As he stood before King Darius, Daniel realised that his King was in despair. The King had tried everything he could think of to get the law changed, but it was no good. Daniel was doomed.

"I hope your God will protect you," whispered the King.

Then, Daniel was taken to a dark, damp cellar just outside the palace walls. In a chamber far below, Daniel could hear the distant roar of hungry lions!

Daniel accepted his punishment bravely. He took the King's hand, and forgave him for the terrible mistake that meant he was about to die.

King Darius stayed right up until the moment his guards led Daniel to the edge of the stone pit. Daniel looked into the darkness below, and took a deep breath. Then the guard pushed him,

and Daniel tumbled...

...into the lions' den.

Daniel landed with a thud and looked up at the small circle of light far above him.

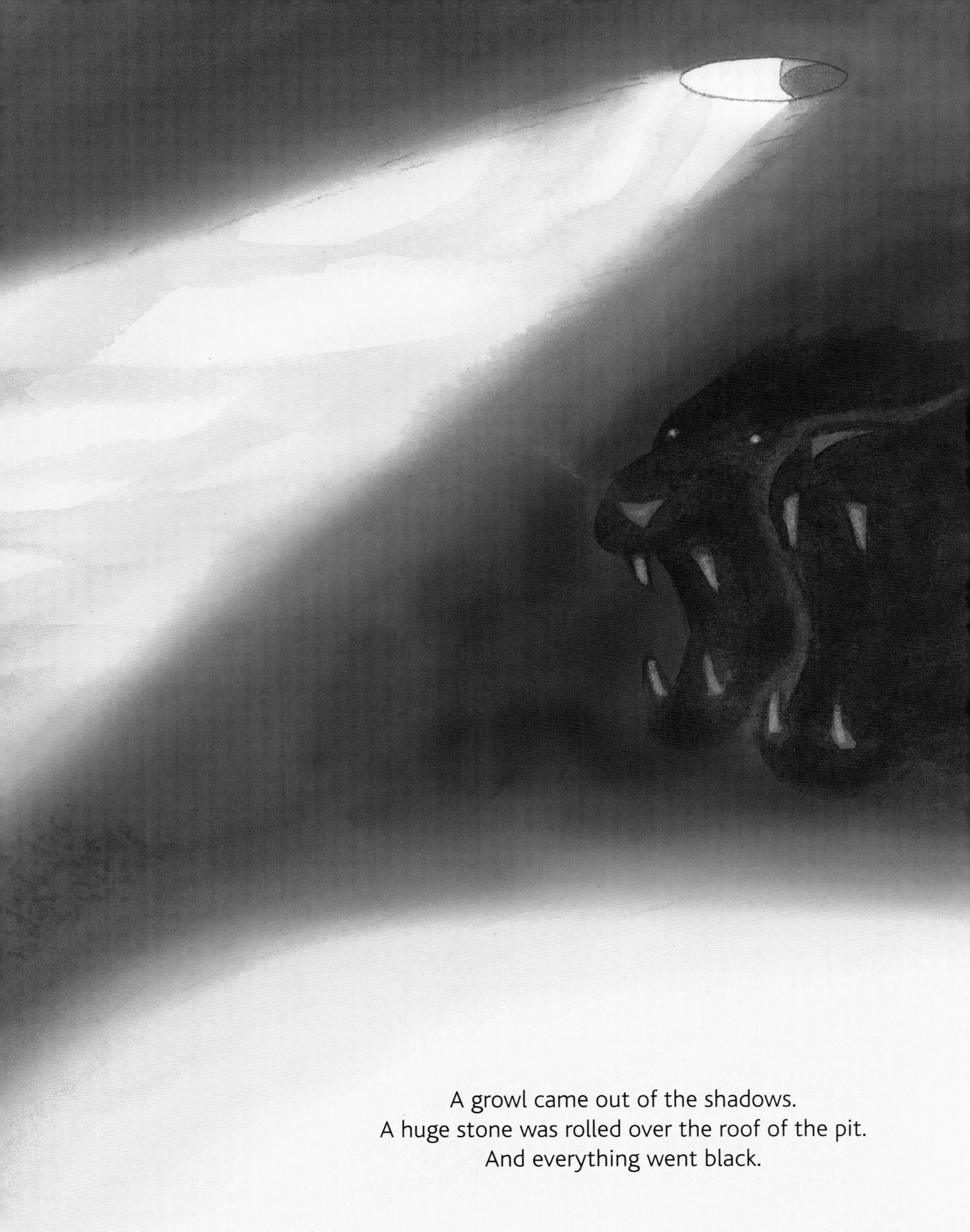

A growl came out of the shadows.
A huge stone was rolled over the roof of the pit.
And everything went black.

King Darius rushed back to the lions' den
at dawn, after a sleepless night.

Using all of his strength, the King rolled back
the heavy stone that covered the pit, and cried,
"Daniel, has your God saved you from the lions?"

There was silence.

Long ago, God asked a young man named Jonah to deliver a message. Jonah was to tell the people who lived in a place called Nineveh to stop being unkind to each other. If they didn't change their wicked ways, God would destroy their city!

Unfortunately, Jonah thought everyone should be punished for their bad behaviour, so instead of delivering the message...

...Jonah sailed away!

He found a ship setting sail for another city, paid the fare, scrambled down to his cabin and jumped straight into bed.

Jonah was so relieved to have avoided carrying out God's plan that he soon fell sound sleep.

But while Jonah snored, a terrible storm began.

Ferocious winds ripped the ship's sails from its mast. Waves taller than buildings crashed over the deck.

The crew threw the cargo overboard to stop
the ship from sinking, but the angry sea
continued to rush in.

"We must find out which person has
sinned, Captain!" shouted one of the
superstitious sailors.
"He's brought us bad luck."

The captain asked the other sailors but it was none of them. Then he woke Jonah, yelling, "If you have done wrong, please ask your God to forgive you before we all drown!"

At once, Jonah realised
that the captain was right.
God was punishing him.

He rushed up to the ship’s deck crying, “It is my fault! I ran away from doing the Lord’s work. Throw me into the sea and the storm will stop.”

Despite trying their hardest to row to safety, the sailors decided they had no choice and they dropped Jonah overboard.

Within moments, a ray of sunlight pierced the black clouds. The foaming sea grew peaceful and the wind lowered to a whisper.

As the skies cleared, the sailors decided
that Jonah's God must have calmed the storm.
They even began to pray to him themselves!

Out at sea, Jonah struggled to the surface, gasping for air.

"Look! He's alive!"
shouted the amazed crew.

Then, something really incredible happened...

...A huge whale rose up from the depths of the water. It opened its enormous jaws and scooped Jonah into its gaping mouth.

In one gulp, Jonah was gone!

With a splutter and a splash, Jonah realised he was inside a whale!

At first he panicked and shouted for help, but any noise Jonah made just echoed around in the darkness.

When he tried to make his way back towards the whale's mouth, he kept slipping down.

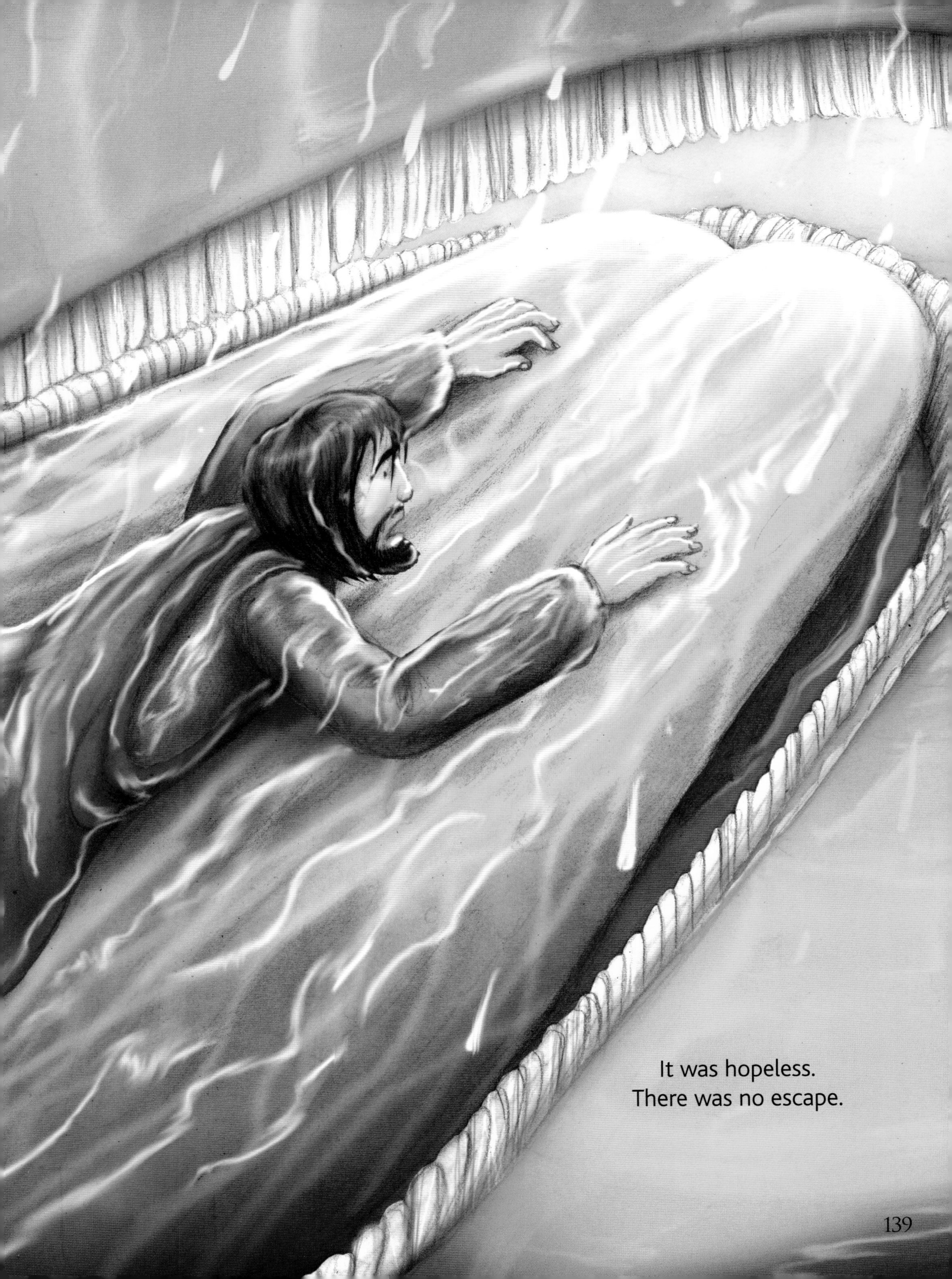

It was hopeless.
There was no escape.

Gradually, Jonah became calm. His eyes grew used to the darkness. The water swishing around his feet wasn't getting deeper. For some reason, this great animal seemed to be keeping him safe.

Jonah decided that God had sent the whale to save him. Immediately, he dropped to his knees and thanked the Lord. As he prayed, Jonah even asked for another chance to do the job he had been given.

Before long, Jonah trusted that God would return him to dry land. For three days and three nights, he waited patiently and prayed.

Finally, something happened...

...The great fish stopped moving. Then there was a sudden rush of air and Jonah was thrown forward on a wave of salty water.

He landed face down on a sandy beach in broad daylight, safe at last!

And this time, Jonah did just as God had asked.

He set off for Nineveh straight away.

Jonah delivered God's message and everyone stopped to listen to him.

"People of Nineveh, you must become better people. If you continue to treat each other badly, the Lord God will destroy your city. But if you pray together and let the Lord love you, you will be saved."

To Jonah's surprise and relief, the people understood his message. He explained how God had saved and forgiven him, and soon, even the King of Nineveh had heard the amazing tale of Jonah and the whale.

Before long, everyone had changed their ways and treated each other with love and respect. They lived peaceful lives and Jonah spent the rest of his days on dry land!

THE NATIVITY STORY

Written by Sasha Morton
Illustrated by Alfredo Belli

Long ago, in Nazareth, an angel appeared to a young woman called Mary.

The Angel Gabriel spoke to her, and he said: "You have been chosen by God to do an important job. You are going to have his son."

Mary told her husband Joseph, who was a good and kind man. They were both happy to do what God wanted and looked forward to the arrival of this special child.

Shortly before the baby was due to be born, Mary and Joseph had to travel to Bethlehem. Mary trusted that God would look after them on their travels and she was right.

Still, it was a hard journey and after several days, they were relieved to see the town of Bethlehem before them.

But once they arrived safely in Bethlehem, they had another problem to face...

...There was not a single room in the town for them to sleep in!

Poor Mary and Joseph went from one side of Bethlehem to the other, but all they heard were the words, "Sorry, there is no room at the inn."

To make things worse, Mary realised that the baby was going to come very soon. What were they going to do?

Tired and hungry, Mary and Joseph trudged to the very last inn in Bethlehem. Yet again, it was full. However, this particular innkeeper took pity on the young couple who stood before him.

"You are welcome to stay in my stable," offered the innkeeper. "My animals are in there too, but it's warm and dry."

On that very night, Mary gave birth and
God's Son came into the world.

In the moment he was born, a star,
brighter than any other in the night sky,
began to sparkle over the stable.

The happy parents wrapped Jesus
in swaddling cloths, and he slept peacefully
on a bed of straw in a manger.

At the same time on a nearby hillside, some shepherds were tending to their sheep. Suddenly, a bright light appeared and an angel stood before them!

"I bring good news," said the angel. "Today in Bethlehem, a baby has been born who is the Son of God. Follow the star and you will find him."

Then, just as quickly as the light had come, it faded. The shepherds looked up in disbelief, and there they saw...

...a dazzling, bright star!

Straight away, the shepherds headed towards the star and soon they arrived at the stable. They crept in and whispered, "An angel told us that the Son of God was here."

Mary and Joseph welcomed the shepherds and showed them their precious child.

The shepherds knelt before
the manger to look
at the baby Jesus.

Not a creature stirred.
All was peaceful.
All was quiet.

In the East, unknown to Mary and Joseph,
three wise men had noticed this new bright star.
They studied the word of God and knew it could only
mean one thing – the King of the Jews,
who would save the world, had been born!

One dusky evening, the wise men began their own journey. The same star guided them night after night...

...through deserted streets...

...over miles of dark desert...

...until they found Mary,
Joseph and Jesus.

Mary and Joseph were happy to welcome these unexpected visitors who had travelled so far to see God's Son.

The three wise men brought gifts of gold,
frankincense and myrrh with them.

They were gifts fit for a king.

Jesus was preaching the word of God to his followers one day, when a man asked him, "Teacher, what must I do to make sure I get to heaven?"

Jesus replied, "You must love God with all your heart, and love your neighbour as you would love yourself."

Then, Jesus told everyone this story.

A Jewish man was walking down the long, steep road from Jerusalem to Jericho.

The path was winding and rocky, yet this was not the reason everyone feared travelling down this path.

It was feared for the many twists and turns
in the road, which meant it was easy for robbers
to lie in wait to steal from people.

Unfortunately, that was exactly what happened to this particular man.

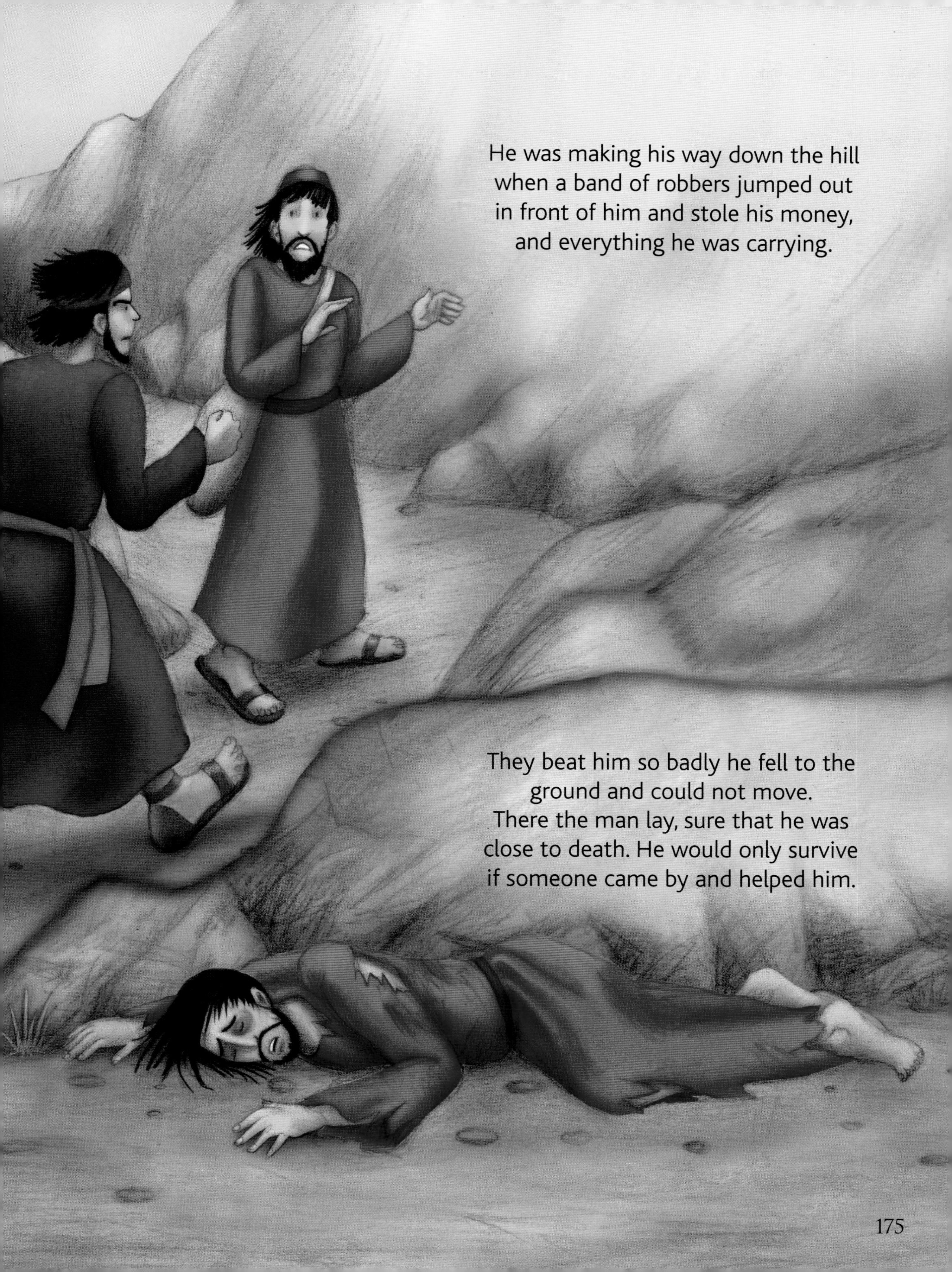

He was making his way down the hill when a band of robbers jumped out in front of him and stole his money, and everything he was carrying.

They beat him so badly he fell to the ground and could not move. There the man lay, sure that he was close to death. He would only survive if someone came by and helped him.

After some time had passed,
the man heard someone coming down
the hill. He would be saved!

He called out for help...

...But the approaching person, a priest, did not stop to help. He took one look at the injured man and crossed over to the other side of the road.

Sadly, the man closed his eyes and waited for death to take him.

Then he heard someone else coming down the hill. He would be saved!

He called out for help...

...But once again, the approaching person, a preacher, crossed over to the other side of the road.

Despairingly, the beaten man closed his eyes once more.

After a while, he heard someone else coming down the hill. Surely this time he would be saved?

But when he looked up, he saw that this traveller was a Samaritan. Because Jewish people did not get along with Samaritan people, the man believed there was no chance that this traveller would stop.

But this Samaritan did not see a Jew, he just saw
a man in pain who needed his help.

Gently, the Samaritan helped
the beaten man to sit up.

He spoke kindly to him. Then, he gave the man something to drink.

He also cleaned and bandaged his wounds as best he could.

Carefully, the Samaritan helped the man on to the back of his own donkey and slowly continued his journey into Jericho.

The man was very grateful
to this stranger – the only
person who had helped him.

The Samaritan took the man to an
inn where he himself was staying.
That night, he cared for the man
and made sure he was comfortable.

Before he went on his way the next morning,
the Samaritan spoke with the innkeeper.

"Please look after this man
while I am gone," he said.

With that, he gave the innkeeper some of his own money and told him, "Take these coins, and on my way back I will repay you for any extra expense his stay here may cost you."

The innkeeper gladly did so and with his help the man recovered,
thanks to the good Samaritan.

When he had finished telling this tale, Jesus asked his followers, "Which of these three, do you think, was a good neighbour to the man who was robbed?"

"The one who took pity on him," answered one of the men.

Jesus replied, "Go, and do the same yourself."

For God wants his children to look after everyone around them, no matter who they are.